CLUES
IN THE ATTIC

www.raintreepublishers.co.uk
Visit our website to find out more information about Raintree books.

To order:
☎ Phone 0845 6044371
🖷 Fax +44 (0) 1865 312263
✉ Email myorders@raintreepublishers.co.uk

Customers from outside the UK please telephone +44 1865 312262

Raintree is an imprint of Capstone Global Library Limited, a company incorporated in England and Wales having its registered office at 7 Pilgrim Street, London, EC4V 6LB – Registered company number: 6695582

Text © Stone Arch Books 2010
First published in hardback and paperback in the United Kingdom by
Capstone Global Library in 2011
The moral rights of the proprietor have been asserted.

UK editor: Siân Smith
Graphic Designer: Emily Harris
Art Director: Bob Lentz
Production Specialist: Michelle Biedscheid
Illustrations by Rémy Simard
Originated by Capstone Global Library Ltd
Printed and bound in China by South China Printing Company Ltd

ISBN 978 1 406 22547 1 (hardback)
15 14 13 12 11
10 9 8 7 6 5 4 3 2 1

ISBN 978 1 406 22552 5 (paperback)
15 14 13 12 11
10 9 8 7 6 5 4 3 2

British Library Cataloguing in Publication Data
Meister, Cari. Clues in the attic. (My first graphic novel)
741.5-dc22
A full catalogue record for this book is available from the British Library.

CLUES IN THE ATTIC

by Cari Meister

illustrated by Rémy Simard

Raintree

HOW TO READ A GRAPHIC NOVEL

Graphic novels are easy to read. Boxes called panels show you how to follow the story. Look at the panels from left to right and top to bottom.

Read the word boxes and speech bubbles from left to right as well. Don't forget the sound and action words in the pictures.

The pictures and the words work together to tell the whole story.

Ben climbed the stairs. He opened the attic door.
He was glad his sister, Sofia, had not seen him.

The attic was cold and dark. There were cobwebs on the walls. Ben was scared.

Ben turned on the light. The light blinked once.
Then it went dark.

The attic smelled funny. There were strange noises.
There were strange shapes.

Ben wanted to leave. But he couldn't. He was looking for something.

Suddenly, the door slammed shut.

Ben opened the door and ran down the stairs.

He tripped and fell.

Sofia heard the noises. She found Ben lying at the bottom of the stairs.

After dinner, Ben decided to go back to the attic.
But first he needed his torch.

The stairs creaked under his feet.

There were cobwebs everywhere! There were also strange noises. It didn't matter. Ben had to be brave.

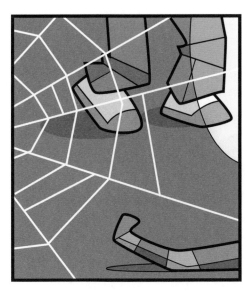 

That's when Ben saw something move.

Ben slammed the attic door and ran.

Sofia was waiting at the bottom of the stairs. Ben could not tell Sofia what he was searching for.

That night, Ben set his alarm and tried to sleep.

He kept having crazy dreams.

Ben's alarm beeped early the next morning.

Ben tiptoed up the attic stairs. This was his last chance to find what he was looking for.

Ben heard more creaking behind him.
Something, or someone, was following him!

What a relief! It was just Sofia.

Ben pulled out a piece of string from his pocket.
He tied a cricket on the end.

That's when Sofia heard the noise. She knew what it was right away.

Sofia picked up her pet snake. She gave it a kiss.

There you are!

SMOOCH!

I left her cage open yesterday.

That's okay. Princess likes a good adventure.

Ben was glad Sofia wasn't mad. Sofia was glad they had found Princess. And Princess was glad to be out of the attic.

ABOUT THE AUTHOR

Cari Meister is the author of many books for children, including the *My Pony Jack* series and *Luther's Halloween*. She lives on a small farm with her husband, four sons, three horses, one dog, and one cat. Cari enjoys running, walking in snowshoes, horse riding, and yoga. She loves to visit libraries and schools.

ABOUT THE ILLUSTRATOR

Artist Rémy Simard began his career as an illustrator in 1980. Today he creates computer-generated illustrations for a large variety of people. He has also written and illustrated more than 30 children's books in both French and English, including *Monsieur Noir et Blanc*, a finalist for Canada's Governor's Prize. To relax, Rémy likes to race around on his motorbike. Rémy lives with his two sons and a cat named Billy.

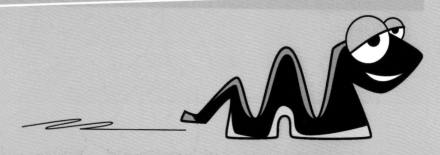

GLOSSARY

ALARM object with a bell or buzzer that wakes people up

ATTIC space in a building just below the roof. Another name for an attic is a loft.

COBWEB net of sticky threads made by a spider

CREAK loud squeaky noise

TIPTOED walked very quietly on the tips of the toes

DISCUSSION QUESTIONS

1. Ben is scared to go in the attic. Talk about something that you are scared to do.

2. Why didn't Ben just tell Sofia that he lost Princess? What would you have done?

3. Have you ever lost something that belonged to someone else?

WRITING PROMPTS

1. Ben finds bats in the attic. Make a list of other creatures that could live in the attic.

2. Make a poster describing the missing snake. Include a picture of the snake and write down her name and what she looks like.

3. Ben has strange dreams about bats. Write a few sentences about a strange dream you have had.

MY 1ST GRAPHIC NOVEL®

THE 1ST STEP INTO GRAPHIC NOVELS

These books are the perfect introduction to the world of graphic novels. Each story uses familiar topics, repeating patterns, and core vocabulary words appropriate for a beginning reader. Combine an entertaining story with comic book panels, exciting action elements, and bright colours and a graphic novel is born!